Piper, Pipe That Song Again!

Weekly Reader Children's Book Club

Presents

Piper, Pipe that Song Again!

Poems for Boys and Girls

Selected by NANCY LARRICK

Illustrated by Kelly Oechsli

RANDOM HOUSE · NEW YORK

Acknowledgments

The editor and publisher acknowledge with thanks permission received from the following to include poems in this collection:

Rowena Bennett for her poem "The Freight Train" which first appeared in *Junior Arts and Activities.*

Beatrice Curtis Brown for her poem "Jonathan Bing," copyright © 1936 by Beatrice Curtis Brown.

Carleton Campbell for "Sally and Manda" by Alice B. Campbell from *Living Poetry,* published by Globe Book Co.

Marchette Chute for her poem "Undersea" which first appeared in *Child Life Magazine.*

Thomas Y. Crowell Company for "June" and "Raccoons" from *Going Barefoot,* copyright © 1960 by the author, Aileen Fisher; Thomas Y. Crowell Company, New York, publishers.

Dodd, Mead & Company and The Bodley Head, Ltd., London, for "I Meant to Do My Work To-day" from *The Lonely Dancer* by Richard LeGallienne; copyright 1913 by Dodd, Mead & Company; published by Dodd, Mead & Company and The Bodley Head, Ltd., London.

Doubleday & Company and The World's Work (1913) Ltd. for "I'd Like to Be a Lighthouse," "Taxis," and "The Animal Store" from *Taxis and Toadstools* by Rachel Field; copyright 1926 by Doubleday & Company, Inc.; reprinted by permission of the publishers.

Dover Publications, Inc., for "I Wish That My Room Had a Floor" from *The Purple Cow and Other Nonsense* by Gelett Burgess.

Dresser, Chapman & Grimes, Inc., for "The Friendly Rock" from *Children Are Poets* by Susan Nichols Pulsifer, published by Dresser, Chapman & Grimes, Inc.

E. P. Dutton & Co., Inc., for "Going to Bed" and "Skiing" (copyright, 1941, by Marchette Chute); "Spring Rain" (copyright, 1946, by Marchette Chute); "Snowflakes" and "Presents" (copyright, 1932, renewal, 1960, by Marchette Chute)—all five poems from the book *Around and About by* Marchette Chute, published 1957 by E. P. Dutton & Co., Inc., and reprinted with their permission. "Shadow Dance" from the book *Fairies and Suchlike* by Ivy O. Eastwick; copyright, 1946, by E. P. Dutton & Co., Inc.; reprinted by permission of the publisher.

cont. on p. 79

Piper, Pipe That Song Again!

Long ago—before radio and television and printed books—wandering musicians went from one village to another, singing songs and reciting poems. Sometimes they would perform in the castle. Sometimes in the courtyard of an inn or in the village square.

From far and near people gathered to hear these minstrels, as they were called. Often the songs were the old ones that people had heard from their fathers and grandfathers. The words were those they had grown up with, and the tunes were almost a part of them.

One of the earliest musical instruments was a hollow reed, called a pipe. It makes a flute-like sound as lilting as the song of an oriole. The Indians of Peru use reed pipes today. In a village market you can buy a pipe for a few pennies. A shepherd boy will pipe a song as he follows his flock across the plains.

We are told that some of the early minstrels used the same kind of reed pipe. The piper would begin to play as he came into town. Children would follow him to catch every note. Men and women would linger to hear the haunting tunes and perhaps to join in with words they knew. If the piper stopped, someone would call for more:

"Piper, pipe that song again!"

Then the wonderful combination of words and music would begin again.

Today we have no wandering poet musicians to bring us the sound of poetry. But we have a legacy from them in our printed books of poetry. Here our poets have recorded their songs for everyone to enjoy. They have used paper and ink instead of reed pipes and their own singing voices. But the melody is there for any reader to hear and to sing as he reads.

By itself the printed page is a silent thing. But as you read the words of a poem, it becomes a musical thing. It may have a gay, laughing melody. Or it may have the soft melody you have heard in swaying grass.

Poems are meant to be read aloud just as songs are meant to be sung aloud. As you read a poem again and again, it becomes part of you. The rhythm seems to flow from you the way a song you love pours out as you sing. And you will want to enjoy it time after time.

Then, indeed, you have become a piper who can "pipe that song again!"

Nancy Larrick

The Piper

Piping down the valleys wild,
  Piping songs of pleasant glee,
On a cloud I saw a child,
  And he laughing said to me:

"Pipe a song about a Lamb!"
  So I piped with merry cheer.
"Piper, pipe that song again;"
  So I piped; he wept to hear.

"Drop thy pipe, thy happy pipe;
  Sing thy songs of happy cheer!"
So I sang the same again,
  While he wept with joy to hear.

"Piper, sit thee down and write
  In a book that all may read."
So he vanished from my sight;
  And I plucked a hollow reed.

And I made a rural pen,
  And I stained the water clear,
And I wrote my happy songs
  Every child may joy to hear.

William Blake

Piper, Pipe That Song Again!

The Secret Song

Who saw the petals
   drop from the rose?
I, said the spider,
But nobody knows.

Who saw the sunset
   flash on the bird?
I, said the fish,
But nobody heard.

Who saw the fog
   come over the sea?
I, said the pigeon,
Only me.

Who saw the first
   green light of the sun?
I, said the night owl,
The only one.

Who saw the moss
   creep over the stone?
I, said the grey fox,
All alone.

Margaret Wise Brown

Ducks' Ditty

All along the backwater,
Through the rushes tall,
Ducks are a-dabbling,
Up tails all!

Ducks' tails, drakes' tails,
Yellow feet a-quiver,
Yellow bills all out of sight
Busy in the river!

Slushy green undergrowth
Where the roach swim
Here we keep our larder,
Cool and full and dim.

Every one for what he likes!
We like to be
Heads down, tails up,
Dabbling free!

High in the blue above
Swifts whirl and call
We are down a-dabbling,
Up tails all!

Kenneth Grahame

I Meant to Do My Work To-Day

I meant to do my work to-day—
    But a brown bird sang in the apple-tree,
And a butterfly flitted across the field,
    And all the leaves were calling me.

And the wind went sighing over the land.
    Tossing the grasses to and fro,
And a rainbow held out its shining hand—
    So what could I do but laugh and go?

Richard LeGallienne

My Heart Leaps Up

My heart leaps up when I behold
  A rainbow in the sky:
So was it when my life began;
So is it now I am a man;
So be it when I shall grow old,
  Or let me die!

              William Wordsworth

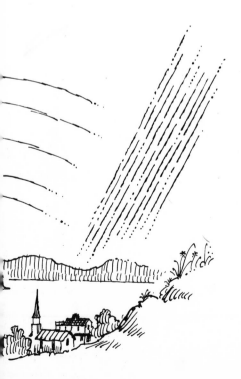

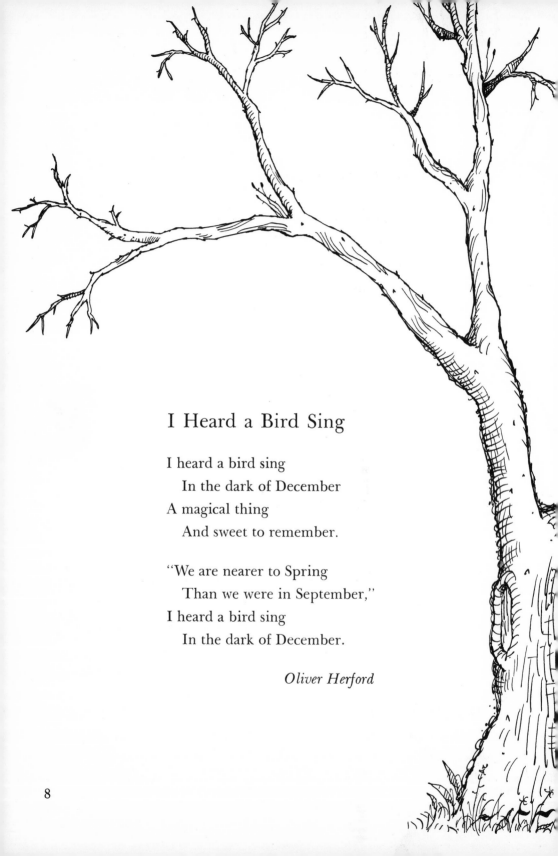

I Heard a Bird Sing

I heard a bird sing
   In the dark of December
A magical thing
   And sweet to remember.

"We are nearer to Spring
   Than we were in September,"
I heard a bird sing
   In the dark of December.

Oliver Herford

For, Lo, the Winter Is Past

For, lo, the winter is past,
The rain is over and gone;
The flowers appear on the earth;
The time of the singing of birds is come,
And the voice of the turtle is heard in our land.

The Song of Solomon

The Caterpillar

Brown and furry
Caterpillar in a hurry,
Take your walk
To the shady leaf, or stalk.

　No toad may spy you,
Hovering bird of prey pass by you;
Spin and die,
To live again a butterfly.

Christina Rossetti

The Tickle Rhyme

"Who's that tickling my back?" said the wall.
　"Me," said a small
Caterpillar. "I'm learning
To crawl."

Ian Serraillier

Little Talk

Don't you think it's probable
that beetles, bugs, and bees
talk about a lot of things—
you know, such things as these:

The kind of weather where they live
in jungles tall with grass
and earthquakes in their villages
whenever people pass!

Of course, we'll never know if bugs
talk very much at all,
because our ears are far too big
for talk that is so small.

Aileen Fisher

The Snake

A snake slipped through the thin green grass
A silver snake
I watched it pass
It moved like a ribbon
Silent as snow.
I think it smiled
As it passed my toe.

Karla Kuskin

A Bird Came down the Walk

A bird came down the walk:
He did not know I saw;
He bit an angle-worm in halves
And ate the fellow, raw.

And then he drank a dew
From a convenient grass,
And then hopped sidewise to the wall
To let a beetle pass.

Emily Dickinson

Grizzly Bear

If you ever, ever, ever meet a grizzly bear,
You must never, never, never ask him where
He is going,
Or what he is doing;
For if you ever, ever, dare
To stop a grizzly bear,
You will never meet another grizzly bear.

Mary Austin

From
Adventures of Isabel

Isabel met an enormous bear,
Isabel, Isabel, didn't care.
The bear was hungry, the bear was ravenous,
The bear's mouth was cruel and cavernous.
The bear said, Isabel, glad to meet you,
How do, Isabel, now I'll eat you!
Isabel, Isabel, didn't worry;
Isabel didn't scream or scurry.
She washed her hands and she straightened her hair up,
Then Isabel quietly ate the bear up.

Ogden Nash

A Pig Tale

Poor Jane Higgins,
She had five piggins,
And one got drowned in the Irish Sea.
Poor Jane Higgins,
She had four piggins,
And one flew over a sycamore tree.
Poor Jane Higgins,
She had three piggins
And one was taken away for pork.
Poor Jane Higgins,
She had two piggins,
And one was sent to the Bishop of Cork.
Poor Jane Higgins,
She had one piggin.
And that was struck by a shower of hail,
Poor Jane Higgins,
She had no piggins,
And that's the end of my little pig tale.

James Reeves

The Reason for the Pelican

The reason for the pelican
Is difficult to see:
His beak is clearly larger
Than there's any need to be.

It's not to bail a boat with—
He doesn't own a boat.
Yet everywhere he takes himself
He has that beak to tote.

It's not to keep his wife in—
His wife has got one, too.
It's not a scoop for eating soup.
It's not an extra shoe.

It isn't quite for anything.
And yet you realize
It's really quite a splendid beak
In quite a splendid size.

John Ciardi

Little Wind

Little wind, blow on the hill-top,
Little wind, blow down the plain;
Little wind, blow up the sunshine,
Little wind, blow off the rain.

Kate Greenaway

Clouds

White sheep, white sheep,
On a blue hill,
When the wind stops
You all stand still.
When the wind blows
You walk away slow.
White sheep, white sheep,
Where do you go?

Christina Rossetti

Windy Wash Day

The wash is hanging on the line
And the wind's blowing—
Dresses all so clean and fine,
Beckoning
And bowing.

Stockings twisting in a dance,
Pajamas very tripping,
And every little pair of pants
Upside down
And skipping.

Dorothy Aldis

Spring Rain

The storm came up so very quick
    It couldn't have been quicker.
I should have brought my hat along,
    I should have brought my slicker.

My hair is wet, my feet are wet,
    I couldn't be much wetter.
I fell into a river once
    But this is even better.

Marchette Chute

April Rain Song

Let the rain kiss you.
Let the rain beat upon your head with silver liquid drops.
Let the rain sing you a lullaby.

The rain makes still pools on the sidewalk.
The rain makes running pools in the gutter.
The rain plays a little sleep-song on our roof at night—

And I love the rain.

Langston Hughes

Spring

The last snow is going,
Brooks are overflowing,
And a sunny wind is blowing
  Swiftly along.

Through the sky birds are blowing,
On earth green is showing,
You can feel earth growing
  So quiet and strong.

A sunny wind is blowing,
Farmer's busy sowing,
Apple trees are snowing,
  And shadows grow long.

Now the wind is slowing,
Cows begin lowing,
Evening clouds are glowing,
  And dusk is full of song.

Harry Behn

The Pasture

I'm going out to clean the pasture spring;
I'll only stop to rake the leaves away
(And wait to watch the water clear, I may);
I shan't be gone long.—You come too.

I'm going out to fetch the little calf
That's standing by the mother. It's so young
It totters when she licks it with her tongue.
I shan't be gone long.—You come too.

Robert Frost

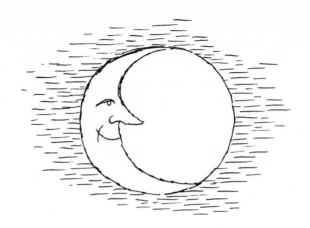

The Horseman

I heard a horseman
   Ride over the hill;
The moon shone clear,
The night was still;
His helm was silver,
   And pale was he;
And the horse he rode
   Was of ivory.

Walter de la Mare

Full of the Moon

It's full of the moon
The dogs dance out
Through brush and bush and bramble.
They howl and yowl
And growl and prowl.
They amble, ramble, scramble.
They rush through brush.
They push through bush.
They yip and yap and hurr.
They lark around and bark around
With prickles in their fur.
They two-step in the meadow.
They polka on the lawn.
Tonight's the night
The dogs dance out
And chase their tails till dawn.

Karla Kuskin

The Moon's the North Wind's Cooky

The Moon's the North Wind's cooky.
He bites it, day by day,
Until there's but a rim of scraps
That crumble all away.

The South Wind is a baker.
He kneads clouds in his den.
And bakes a crisp new moon *that...greedy*
North...Wind...eats...again!

Vachel Lindsay

The Night Will Never Stay

The night will never stay,
The night will still go by,
Though with a million stars
You pin it to the sky;
Though you bind it with the blowing wind
And buckle it with the moon,
The night will slip away
Like sorrow or a tune.

Eleanor Farjeon

February Twilight

I stood beside a hill
  Smooth with new-laid snow,
A single star looked out
  From the cold evening glow.

There was no other creature
  That saw what I could see—
I stood and watched the evening star
  As long as it watched me.

Sara Teasdale

Stopping by Woods on a Snowy Evening

Whose woods these are I think I know.
His house is in the village though;
He will not see me stopping here
To watch his woods fill up with snow.

The little horse must think it queer
To stop without a farmhouse near
Between the woods and frozen lake
The darkest evening of the year.

He gives his harness bells a shake
To ask if there is some mistake.
The only other sound's the sweep
Of easy wind and downy flake.

The woods are lovely dark and deep.
But I have promises to keep,
And miles to go before I sleep,
And miles to go before I sleep.

Robert Frost

Snowflakes

I once thought that snowflakes were feathers
   And that they came falling down
When the Moon Lady feathered her chickens
   And shook out her silver gown.

And then I began to look closer,
   And now I know just what they are—
I caught one today in my mitten,
   And there was a baby star.

Marchette Chute

Skiing

I'm very good at skiing.
　　I have a kind of knack
For I can do it frontways
　　And also on my back.
And when I reach the bottom
　　I give a sudden flop
And dig myself in sideways,
　　And that's the way I stop.

Marchette Chute

Snow in the City

Snow is out of fashion,
    But it still comes down,
To whiten all the buildings
    In our town;
To dull the noise of traffic;
    To dim each glaring light
With star-shaped feathers
    Of frosty white.
And not the tallest building
    Halfway up the sky;
Or all the trains and busses,
    And taxis scudding by;
And not a million people,
    Not one of them at all,
Can do a thing about the snow
    But let it fall!

Rachel Field

City

In the morning the city
Spreads its wings
Making a song
In stone that sings.

In the evening the city
Goes to bed
Hanging lights
About its head.

Langston Hughes

Fog

The fog comes
on little cat feet.

It sits looking
over harbor and city
on silent haunches
and then moves on.

Carl Sandburg

City Lights

Into the endless dark
The lights of the buildings shine,
Row upon twinkling row,
Line upon glistening line.
Up and up they mount
Till the tallest seems to be
The topmost taper set
On a towering Christmas tree.

Rachel Field

Motor Cars

From a city window, 'way up high,
I like to watch the cars go by.
They look like burnished beetles black,
That leave a little muddy track
Behind them as they slowly crawl.
Sometimes they do not move at all
But huddle close with hum and drone
As though they feared to be alone.
They grope their way through fog and night
With the golden feelers of their light.

Rowena Bastin Bennett

Taxis

Ho, for taxis green or blue,
   Hi, for taxis red,
They roll along the Avenue
   Like spools of colored thread!

Jack-'o-Lantern yellow,
Orange as the moon,
Greener than the greenest grass,
Ever grew in June.
Gayly striped or checked in squares,
Wheels that twinkle bright,
Don't you think that taxis make
A very pleasant sight?
Taxis shiny in the rain,
Scudding through the snow,
Taxis flashing back the sun
Waiting in a row.

Ho, for taxis red and green
   Ho, for taxis blue,
I wouldn't be a private car
   In sober black, would you?

Rachel Field

J's the Jumping Jay-Walker

J's the jumping Jay-walker,
   A sort of human jeep.
He crosses where the lights are red.
   Before he looks, he'll leap!
Then many a wheel
Begins to squeal,
   And many a brake to slam.
He turns your knees to jelly
   And the traffic into jam.

Phyllis McGinley

F Is the Fighting Firetruck

F is the Fighting Firetruck
   That's painted a flaming red.
When the signals blast
It follows fast
   When the chief flies on ahead.
And buses pull to the curbing
   At the siren's furious cry,
For early or late
They have to wait
   When the Firetruck flashes by.

Phyllis McGinley

The Freight Train

The slow freight wriggles along the rail
With a red caboose for a lashing tail,
With a one-eyed engine for a head
The slow freight follows the river bed.

He moves like a snake that has grown too fat,
One that has swallowed a frog and a rat;
But a giant of snakes is the moving freight
And these are some of the things he ate:

A herd of sheep and a hundred hens
And dozens of pigs with crates for pens
And horses and cows by the sixes and tens;
And these are some of the things he drank:
Oil and gasoline by the tank,
Milk by the gallon and cream by the pail—
No wonder he moves at the pace of a snail.

Rowena Bastin Bennett

Travel

The railroad track is miles away,
  And the day is loud with voices speaking,
Yet there isn't a train goes by all day
  But I hear its whistle shrieking.

All night there isn't a train goes by,
  Though the night is still for sleep and dreaming
But I see its cinders red on the sky
  And hear its engine steaming.

My heart is warm with the friends I make,
  And better friends I'll not be knowing,
Yet there isn't a train I wouldn't take,
  No matter where it's going.

Edna St. Vincent Millay

Song for a Little House

I'm glad our house is a little house,
Not too tall nor too wide:
I'm glad the hovering butterflies
Feel free to come inside.

Our little house is a friendly house,
It is not shy or vain;
It gossips with the talking trees
And makes friends with the rain.

And quick leaves cast a shimmer of green
Against our whited walls,
And in the phlox, the courteous bees
Are paying duty calls.

Christopher Morley

Undersea

Beneath the waters
  Green and cool
The mermaids keep
  A swimming school.

The oysters trot;.
  The lobsters prance;
The dolphins come
  To join the dance.

But the jellyfish
  Who are rather small,
Can't seem to learn
  The steps at all.

Marchette Chute

I'd Like to Be a Lighthouse

I'd like to be a lighthouse
   All scrubbed and painted white.
I'd like to be a lighthouse
   And stay awake all night
To keep my eye on everything
   That sails my patch of sea;
I'd like to be a lighthouse
   With the ships all watching me.

Rachel Field

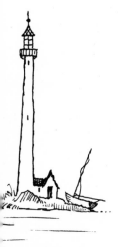

The Friendly Rock

There's a friendly rock down by the shore—
He's teaching me to swim—
I'm not afraid—
Not any more!
I just hold on to him!

Susan Nichols Pulsifer

Daddy Fell into the Pond

Everyone grumbled. The sky was grey.
We had nothing to do and nothing to say.
We were nearing the end of a dismal day,
And there seemed to be nothing beyond,

THEN

Daddy fell into the pond!

And everyone's face grew merry and bright,
And Timothy danced for sheer delight.
"Give me the camera, quick, oh quick!
He's crawling out of the duckweed." *Click!*

Then the gardener suddenly slapped his knee,
And doubled up, shaking silently,
And the ducks all quacked as if they were daft
And it sounded as if the old drake laughed.

O, there wasn't a thing that didn't respond

WHEN

Daddy fell into the pond!

Alfred Noyes

June

The day is warm
and a breeze is blowing,
the sky is blue
and its eye is glowing,
and everything's new
and green and growing. . . .

My shoes are off
and my socks are showing. . . .

My socks are off. . . .

Do you know how I'm going?
BAREFOOT!

Aileen Fisher

Raccoons

Did you ever look
near a wildish brook
or a green-eyed pond
with a wood beyond
and see (on the bank
where the grass grows rank)
a five-toed track?
Hands in front
and feet in back
like an all-four child
in a place so wild?
There a raccoon
on a late afternoon
or under the light
of a lantern moon
went looking for frogs
and mice to eat...
in his barefoot feet.
That's where he walked
in the thick black ooze
without any shoes.

And so will I
when the sun is high
in the wide June sky!

Aileen Fisher

Old Smokie

It's raining, it's hailing,
   The stars give no light.
My horses can't travel
   This dark stormy night.

Go put them in the stable
   And give them some hay,
Come sit in my cabin
   As long as you stay.

My horses aren't hungry
   They won't eat your hay,
And I must be riding
   Until it is day.

I'll go to Old Smokie,
   The mountain so high,
I'll meet all my friends in
   The land in the sky.

Unknown

The Woodpecker

The woodpecker pecked out a little round hole
And made him a house in the telephone pole
One day when I watched he poked out his head,
And he had on a hood and a collar of red.
When the streams of rain pour out of the sky,
And the sparkles of lightning go flashing by,
And the big, big wheels of thunder roll,
He can snuggle back in the telephone pole.

Elizabeth Madox Roberts

The Rabbit

When they said the time to hide was mine,
I hid back under a thick grape vine.

And while I was still for the time to pass,
O little gray thing came out of the grass.

He hopped his way through the melon bed
And sat down close by a cabbage head.

He sat down close where I could see,
And his big still eyes looked hard at me.

His big eyes bursting out of the rim,
And I looked back very hard at him.

Elizabeth Madox Roberts

The Snare

I hear a sudden cry of pain!
   There is a rabbit in a snare;
Now I hear the cry again,
   But I cannot tell from where.

But I cannot tell from where
   He is calling out for aid;
Crying on the frightened air,
   Making everything afraid.

Making everything afraid,
   Wrinkling up his little face,
As he cries again for aid;
   And I cannot find the place!

And I cannot find the place
   Where his paw is in the snare:
Little one! Oh, little one!
   I am searching everywhere!

James Stephens

The Ship of Rio

There was a ship of Rio
   Sailed out into the blue,
And nine and ninety monkeys
   Were all her jovial crew.
From bos'un to the cabin boy,
   From quarter to caboose,
There weren't a stitch of calico
   To breech 'em—tight or loose;
From spar to deck, from deck to keep,
   From barnacle to shroud,
There weren't one pair of reach-me-downs
   To all that jabbering crowd.
But wasn't it a gladsome sight,
   When roared the deep-sea gales,
To see them reef her fore and aft,
   A-swinging by their tails!
Oh, wasn't it a gladsome sight,
   When glassy calm did come,
To see them squatting tailor-wise
   Around a keg of rum!
Oh, wasn't it a gladsome sight,
   When in she sailed to land,
To see them all a-scampering skip
   For nuts across the sand!

Walter de la Mare

The Animal Fair

I went to the animal fair,
The birds and the beasts were there.
The old raccoon by the light of the moon,
Was combing his auburn hair.
The monkey, he got drunk,
And sat on the elephant's trunk.
The elephant sneezed and fell on his knees,
But what became of the monk, the monk, the monk?

Unknown

The Monkeys and the Crocodile

Five little monkeys
    Swinging from a tree;
Teasing Uncle Crocodile
    Merry as can be.
Swinging high, swinging low,
    Swinging left and right:
"Dear Uncle Crocodile,
    Come and take a bite!"

Five little monkeys
    Swinging in the air;
Heads up, tails up,
    Little do they care.
Swinging up, swinging down,
    Swinging far and near:
"Poor Uncle Crocodile,
    Aren't you hungry, dear?"

Four little monkeys
Sitting in the tree;
Heads down, tails down,
Dreary as can be.
Weeping loud, weeping low,
Crying to each other:
"Wicked Uncle Crocodile,
To gobble up our brother!"

Laura E. Richards

How Doth the Little Crocodile

How doth the little crocodile
Improve his shining tail,
And pour the waters of the Nile
On every shining scale!

How cheerfully he seems to grin,
How neatly spreads his claws,
And welcomes little fishes in,
With gently smiling jaws!

Lewis Carroll

In the Fashion

A lion has a tail and a very fine tail,
And so has an elephant, and so has a whale,
And so has a crocodile, and so has a quail—
　　They've all got tails but me.

If I had a sixpence I would buy one;
I'd say to the shopman, "Let me try one";
I'd say to the elephant, "This is *my* one."
　　They'd all come round to see.

Then I'd say to the lion, "Why *you've* got a tail!
And so has the elephant, and so has the whale!
And, look! There's a crocodile! *He's* got a tail!
　　You've all got tails like me!"

　　　　　　　　　　　　A. A. Milne

Holding Hands

Elephants walking
Along the trails

Are holding hands
By holding tails

Trunks and tails
Are handy things

When elephants walk
In Circus rings.

Elephants work
And elephants play

And elephants walk
And feel so gay.

And when they walk—
It never fails

They're holding hands
By holding tails.

Lenore M. Link

The Animal Store

If I had a hundred dollars to spend,
  Or maybe a little more,
I'd hurry as fast as my legs would go
  Straight to the animal store.

I wouldn't say, "How much for this or that?"
  "What kind of a dog is he?"
I'd buy as many as rolled an eye,
  Or wagged a tail at me!

I'd take the hound with the drooping ears
  That sits by himself alone;
Cockers and Cairns and wobbly pups
  For to be my very own.

I might buy a parrot all red and green,
  And the monkey I saw before,
If I had a hundred dollars to spend,
  Or maybe a little more.

Rachel Field

The Hairy Dog

My dog's so furry I've not seen
His face for years and years:
His eyes are buried out of sight,
I only guess his ears.

When people ask me for his breed,
I do not know or care:
He has the beauty of them all
Hidden beneath his hair.

Herbert Asquith

Presents

I wanted a rifle for Christmas,
   I wanted a bat and a ball,
I wanted some skates and a bicycle,
   But I didn't want mittens at all.

     I wanted a whistle
        And I wanted a kite.
     I wanted a pocketknife
        That shut up tight.
     I wanted some boots
     And I wanted a kit,
But I didn't want mittens one little bit.

I told them I didn't like mittens,
   I told them as plain as plain.
I told them I didn't WANT mittens,
   And they've given me mittens again!

          Marchette Chute

Missing

Has anybody seen my mouse?

I opened his box for half a minute,
Just to make sure he was really in it,
And while I was looking, he jumped outside!
I tried to catch him, I tried, I tried....
I think he's somewhere about the house.
Has *anyone* seen my mouse?

Uncle John, have you seen my mouse?

Just a small sort of mouse, a dear little brown one,
He came from the country, he wasn't a town one,
So he'll feel all lonely in a London street;
Why, what could he possibly find to eat?

He must be somewhere. I'll ask Aunt Rose:
Have you seen a mouse with a woffelly nose?
Oh, somewhere about—
He's just got out....

Hasn't *anybody* seen my mouse?

A. A. Milne

Every Time I Climb a Tree

Every time I climb a tree
Every time I climb a tree
Every time I climb a tree
I scrape a leg
Or skin a knee
And every time I climb a tree
I find some ants
Or dodge a bee
And get the ants
All over me

And every time I climb a tree
Where have you been?
They say to me
But don't they know that I am free
Every time I climb a tree?
I like it best
To spot a nest
That has an egg
Or maybe three

And then I skin
The other leg
But every time I climb a tree
I see a lot of things to see
Swallows, rooftops and TV
And all the fields and farms there be
Every time I climb a tree
Though climbing may be good for ants
It isn't awfully good for pants
But still it's pretty good for me
Every time I climb a tree.

David McCord

The Swing

How do you like to go up in a swing,
   Up in the air so blue?
Oh, I do think it the pleasantest thing
   Ever a child can do!

Up in the air and over the wall,
   Till I can see so wide,
Rivers and trees and cattle and all
   Over the countryside—

Till I look down on the garden green,
   Down on the roof so brown—
Up in the air I go flying again,
   Up in the air and down!

Robert Louis Stevenson

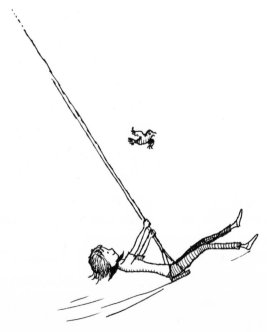

Mumps

I had a feeling in my neck,
And on the sides were two big bumps;
I couldn't swallow anything
At all because I had the mumps.

And Mother tied it with a piece,
And then she tied up Will and John,
And no one else but Dick was left
That didn't have a mump rag on.

He teased at us and laughed at us,
And said whenever he went by,
"It's vinegar and lemon drops
And pickles!" just to make us cry.

But Tuesday Dick was very sad
And cried because his neck was sore,
And not a one said sour things
To anybody any more.

Elizabeth Madox Roberts

Going to Bed

I'm always told to hurry up—
  Which I'd be glad to do,
If there were not so many things
  That need attending to.

But first I have to find my towel
  Which fell behind the rack,
And when a pillow's thrown at me
  I have to throw it back.

And then I have to get the things
  I need in bed with me.
Like marbles and my birthday train
  And Pete the chimpanzee.

I have to see my polliwog
  Is safely in its pan,
And stand a minute on my head
  To be quite sure I can.

I have to bounce upon my bed
  To see if it will sink,
And then when I am covered up
  I find I need a drink.

                    Marchette Chute

Whistles

I want to learn to whistle,
I've always wanted to.
I fix my mouth to do it but
The whistle won't come through.

I think perhaps it's stuck, and so
I try it once again.
Can people swallow whistles?
Where is my whistle then?

Dorothy Aldis

Jonathan Bing

Poor old Jonathan Bing
Went out in his carriage to visit the King,
But everyone pointed and said, "Look at that!
Jonathan Bing has forgotten his hat!"
(He's forgotten his hat!)

Poor old Jonathan Bing
Went home and put on a hat for the King,
But up by the palace a soldier said, "Hi!
You can't see the King; you've forgotten your tie!"
(He'd forgotten his tie!)

Poor old Jonathan Bing,
He put on a *beautiful* tie for the King,
But when he arrived an Archbishop said, "Ho!
You can't come to court in pyjamas, you know!"

Poor old Jonathan Bing
Went home and addressed a short note to the King:
    If you please will excuse me
    I won't come to tea;
    For home's the best place for
    All people like me!

Beatrice Curtis Brown

Some Cook!

Johnny made a custard
In the pepper pot.
Flavored it with mustard,
Put in quite a lot
Of garlic fried in olive oil,
Brought the custard to a boil,
Ate it up and burned his tongue—

You shouldn't cook when you're too young!

John Ciardi

There Was a Crooked Man

There was a crooked man,
   And he went a crooked mile;
He found a crooked sixpence
   Upon a crooked stile:
He bought a crooked cat,
   Which caught a crooked mouse,
And they all lived together
   In a little crooked house.

Unknown

There Was an Old Man of Blackheath

There was an old man of Blackheath,
Who sat on his set of false teeth.
   Said he, with a start,
   "Oh, Lord, bless my heart!
I've bitten myself underneath!"

Unknown

From
Father William

"You are old, Father William," the young man said,
   "And your hair has become very white;
And yet you incessantly stand on your head—
   Do you think, at your age, it is right?"

"In my youth," Father William replied to his son,
   "I feared it might injure the brain;
But now that I'm perfectly sure I have none,
   Why, I do it again and again."

Lewis Carroll

The Cats of Kilkenny

There were once two cats of Kilkenny,
Each thought there was one cat too many;
So they fought and they fit,
And they scratched and they bit,
Till, excepting their nails
And the tips of their tails,
Instead of two cats, there weren't any.

Unknown

Sally and Manda

Sally and Manda are two little lizards
  Who gobble up flies in their two little gizzards.
They live by a toadstool near two little hummocks
  And crawl all around on their two little stomachs.

Alice B. Campbell

I Wish That My Room Had a Floor

I wish that my room had a floor;
I don't care so much for a door.
   But this walking around
    Without touching the ground
Is getting to be quite a bore.

Gelett Burgess

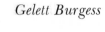

My Shadow

I have a little shadow that goes in and out with me,
But what can be the use of him is more than I can see.
He is very, very like me from the heels up to the head;
And I see him jump before me, when I jump into my bed.

The funniest thing about him is the way he likes to grow—
Not at all like proper children, which is always very slow;
For he sometimes shoots up taller like an India-rubber
   ball,
And he sometimes gets so little that there's none of him at
   all.

He hasn't got a notion of how children ought to play,
And can only make a fool of me in every sort of way.
He stays so close beside me, he's a coward you can see;
I'd think it shame to stick to nursie as that shadow
   sticks to me!

One morning, very early, before the sun was up,
I rose and found the shining dew on every buttercup;
But my lazy little shadow, like an arrant sleepy-head,
Had stayed at home behind me and was fast asleep in bed.

Robert Louis Stevenson

Shadow Dance

O Shadow,
Dear Shadow,
Come, Shadow,
And dance!
On the wall
In the firelight
Let both of
Us prance!
I raise my
Arms, thus!
And you raise
Your arms, so!
And dancing
And leaping
And laughing
We go!
From the wall
To the ceiling
From ceiling
To wall,
Just you and
I, Shadow,
And none else
At all.

Ivy O. Eastwick

Little Donkey Close Your Eyes

Little Donkey on the hill
Standing there so very still
Making faces at the skies
Little Donkey close your eyes.

Little Monkey in the tree
Swinging there so merrily
Throwing cocoanuts at the skies
Little Monkey close your eyes.

Silly Sheep that slowly crop
Night has come and you must stop
Chewing grass beneath the skies
Silly Sheep now close your eyes.

Little Pig that squeals about
Make no noises with your snout
No more squealing to the skies
Little Pig now close your eyes.

Wild young birds that sweetly sing
Curve your heads beneath your wing
Dark night covers all the skies
Wild young birds now close your eyes.

Old black cat down in the barn
Keeping five small kittens warm
Let the wind blow in the skies
Dear old black cat close your eyes.

Little child all tucked in bed
Looking such a sleepy head
Stars are quiet in the skies
Little child now close your eyes.

Margaret Wise Brown

Acknowledgments

Continued from page iv

E. P. Dutton & Co., Inc., and Methuen & Co., Ltd., for "Missing" and "In the Fashion" from *When We Were Very Young* by A. A. Milne; copyright, 1924, by E. P. Dutton & Co., Inc., renewal, 1952, by A. A. Milne; reprinted by permission of the publishers.

E. P. Dutton & Co., Inc., and Oxford University Press, London, for "A Pig Tale" from *The Blackbird in the Lilac* by James Reeves; published 1959 by E. P. Dutton & Co., Inc.; reprinted by permission of the publishers.

Norma Millay Ellis for "Travel" from *Collected Poems* by Edna St. Vincent Millay, published by Harper & Row; copyright 1921, 1948 by Edna St. Vincent Millay; by permission of Norma Millay Ellis.

Aileen Fisher for "Little Talk" from *That's Why* published by Thomas Nelson & Sons, New York, 1946.

Follett Publishing Company for "Motor Cars" from *Songs From Around a Toadstool Table* by Rowena Bastin Bennett; copyright © 1930, 1937.

Harcourt, Brace & World, Inc., for "Spring" from *The Little Hill*, copyright, 1949, by Harry Behn; reprinted by permission of Harcourt, Brace & World, Inc.

Harper & Row, Publishers, Incorporated, for "Full of the Moon" and "The Snake" from *In the Middle of the Trees* by Karla Kuskin; copyright © 1958 by Karla Kuskin.

Helen B. Herford for "I Heard a Bird Sing" by Oliver Herford.

Holt, Rinehart & Winston, Inc., and Laurence Pollinger Limited for "Stopping by Woods on a Snowy Evening" and "The Pasture" from *Complete Poems of Robert Frost;* copyright 1923, 1930, 1939 by Holt, Rinehart and Winston, Inc.; copyright renewed 1951 by Robert Frost. "Fog" from *Chicago Poems* by Carl Sandburg; copyright 1916 by Holt, Rinehart and Winston, Inc.; copyright renewed 1944 by Carl Sandburg; reprinted by permission of Holt, Rinehart and Winston, Inc., and Laurence Pollinger Limited.

Houghton Mifflin Company for "Grizzly Bear" from *The Children Sing in the Far West* by Mary Austin.

Langston Hughes for "City," reprinted by permission of the author from *Golden Slippers; An Anthology of Negro Poetry*, edited by Arna Bontemps, published by Harper & Row, Publishers, Inc.

Alfred A. Knopf, Inc., for "April Rain Song" from *The Dream Keeper* by Langston Hughes; copyright 1932 by Alfred A. Knopf, Inc.

J. B. Lippincott Company for "Some Cook!" from *The Man Who Sang the Sillies* by John Ciardi; copyright © 1961 by John Ciardi. "The Reason for the Pelican" from *The Reason for the Pelican* by John Ciardi: copyright 1955 by Curtis Publishing Company. "Song for a Little House" from *Poems* by Christopher Morley; copyright 1921, 1949 by Christopher Morley. Published by J. B. Lippincott Company.

J. B. Lippincott Company and Harold Ober Associates Incorporated for "The Night Will Never Stay" from Eleanor Farjeon's *Poems for Children;* copyright 1920 by E. P.

Index of Titles

Index of Authors

ABOUT THE AUTHOR:

NANCY LARRICK was born in Winchester, Virginia, and became a classroom teacher there immediately after her graduation from Goucher College. "I have always loved poetry," she says, "and I read it to my pupils almost every day. I found all of them enjoyed poetry once they had heard it read aloud. After that they clamored for poems that were simple enough for them to read without faltering and intriguing enough to go back to again and again."

Since her first days of teaching in Virginia, Miss Larrick has received her master's and doctor's degrees, has been an editor of children's magazines and books, and has taught in the graduate school of education in New York University, Indiana University, the Bank Street College of Education and Lehigh University. She has served as president of the International Reading Association of which she is an Honorary Member, has been editor of *The Reading Teacher*, and is a member of the National Conference on Research in English.

Dr. Larrick is widely known as the author of *A Parent's Guide to Children's Reading*, which was sponsored by the National Book Committee and won the 1959 Edison Foundation Award. Her other books include *A Teacher's Guide to Children's Books* and *A Parent's Guide to Children's Education*.

With her husband, Alexander L. Crosby, Miss Larrick lives in an old stone farmhouse near Quakertown, Pennsylvania.